GIVERNY
A Book of Days

Pomegranate Calendars & Books

San Francisco

Published by Pomegranate
Box 6099
Rohnert Park, California 94927

Pomegranate Europe Ltd.
Fullbridge House, Fullbridge
Maldon, Essex CM9 4LE
England

ISBN 0-87654-429-4
Pomegranate Catalog No. A529

Cover design by Patty Burke
Book design by Stephen Kruse

Printed in Korea

07 06 05 04 03 02 01 00 99 98 26 25 24 23 22 21 20 19 18 17

*g*iverny is a small village forty miles northwest of Paris that nestles between the east bank of the Seine and the north bank of the Epte River. In 1883 Claude Monet brought his family to Giverny and rented the house and property that was to be his home for the final forty-three years of his life. By 1890 Monet was doing well enough to purchase this property, and in 1893 he added the parcel that he was to convert into the famous waterlily pond with Japanese bridge. Monet completed hundreds of canvasses during his many years at Giverny, but he claimed that his carefully tended flower and waterlily gardens were his greatest masterpieces. They certainly served as the subjects for most of his later paintings, most notably, of course, his waterlily creations.

Monet within his long life came to be respected by other painters as the master, leading Impressionist. For this reason, and because Giverny was in itself an idyllic, pastoral community, easily accessible from Paris, many of them visited Giverny. Monet did not teach formally, but he allowed some visitors. Summering in Giverny became routine for many French painters, and several American Impressionists made more than one sojourn there.

Today, Monet's estate at Giverny is completely restored, with the houses and gardens preserved according to Monet's original designs. It is frequented by visitors still – people who are interested in either Monet the painter or Monet the gardener, or both. Giverny maintains its magical appeal, drawing the visually sensitive within its boundaries.

This book of days communicates that appeal through a diverse collection of images. Many of Monet's Giverny paintings are reproduced here along with paintings created at Giverny by other artists such as Theodore Robinson, Frederick Carl Frieseke, Guy Rose, Lawton Parker, Theodore Wendel and Louis Ritman. Interspersed among these exquisite paintings are the vibrant, full color photographs of the present day gardens at Giverny, photographed by Elizabeth Murray. Murray lived at Monet's estate for a year in 1985, working as a gardener, and she returns about once a year to rephotograph the resplendent flowers. Finally, this book of days includes black and white photographs of Claude Monet himself, at his Giverny home.

Had Monet not settled in Giverny, it may not have become the thriving artists' community that it did. The powerful effect his paintings had on his contemporaries as well as future generations is well documented – Monet continues to be the most popular French Impressionist today. His home has clearly had the same long-lasting effect, inspiring painters and photographers throughout the world. Here, then, a tribute – to Giverny.

Sources

Boyle, Richard J. *American Impressionism*. Boston: New York Graphic Society, 1974.

Gerdts, William H. *American Impressionism*. New York: Abbeville Press, 1984.

Hoopes, Donelson F. *The American Impressionists*. New York: Watson-Guptill Publications, 1972.

Joyes, Claire. *Claude Monet: Life at Giverny*. New York: The Vendome Press, 1985.

Love, Richard H. *Theodore Earl Butler: Emergence from Monet's Shadow*. Chicago: Haase-Mumm Publishing Company, Inc., 1985.

The Metropolitan Museum of Art. *Monet's Years at Giverny: Beyond Impressionism*. New York: The Metropolitan Museum of Art, 1978.

Stuckey, Charles F., ed. *Monet: A Retrospective*. New York: Hugh Lauter Levin Associates, Inc., 1985.

Terra Museum of American Art. *A Proud Heritage: Two Centuries of American Art*. Chicago: Terra Museum of American Art, 1987.

Claude Monet paints the same picture many times, and never – this became clear as we were looking at the dazzling *Water Lilies* – never is there the slightest trace of fatigue. With some of his canvases one could swear that they had been dashed off in a single afternoon, whereas in reality the master has sometimes worked on them for several years."

Louis Vauxcelles, "An Afternoon Visit with Claude Monet," *L'Art et les Artistes,* December, 1905

Claude Monet (French, 1840-1926)
Waterlilies, 1903
Oil on canvas, 32 x 40 in.
The Dayton Art Institute
Gift of Mr. Joseph Rubin, 53.11

January

1 _____

2 _____

3 _____

4 _____

5 _____

6 _____

7 _____

"The garden is not the luxury hobby of some property owner, created to show off the quality of his seeds; it is the retreat of an artist, and the flowers are his companions. He wants to be able to caress them as he goes by, to feel them close to him, surrounding him, friendly and beneficent parts of his life."

Maurice Kahn, "Claude Monet's Garden," *Le Temps,* June 7, 1904

Claude Monet (French, 1840-1926)
Monet's Garden at Giverny, 1900
Oil on canvas, 31^5/$_8$ x 35^7/$_8$ in.
Musée d'Orsay, Paris

8 _____

9 _____

10 _____

11 _____

12 _____

13 _____

14 _____

*r*obinson moved next door to Monet in 1888 and lived there until 1892. He enjoyed an intimate friendship with the famous Impressionist, unlike most Americans who visited Giverny. While he never adopted the Impressionists' techniques and theories completely, his style definitively changed concurrent with his move to Giverny, incorporating the Impressionistic aesthetic.

Theodore Robinson (American, 1852-96)
In the Garden, c. 1889
Oil on canvas, 18 x 22 in.
Westmoreland Museum of Art
William A. Coulter Fund, 58.36

January

15

16

17

18

19

20

21

t he zig-zag walk up the Grand Allée is created by the creeping nasturtiums across the gravel path. Monet painted this scene many times, even when he was almost blind. The Grand Allée is planted with over 10,000 annuals, perennials and bulbs, all planned to bloom in continuous color-coordinated profusion.

Photo by Elizabeth Murray

22

23

24

25

26

27

28

"My garden is my very own creation, grown slowly and tended with never-ceasing love. When I arrived four years ago I found only a farmhouse, and a meagre garden with some fruit trees. I bought the house, enlarged it bit by bit and adapted the place to my needs. I dug the earth, planted flowers and drew out weeds. In the evening the children watered the garden."

Monet, 1887

Claude Monet in his garden, c. 1923.
Photo courtesy of the Musée Claude Monet

29

30

31

1

2

3

4

"*a*fter painting, Monet's chief recreation is gardening. In his domain at Giverny, and in his Japanese water-garden across the road and railway (which to his lasting sorrow cuts his little world in twain), each season of the year brings its appointed and distinguishing colour scheme. Nowhere else can be found such a prodigal display of rare and marvelously beautiful colour effects, arranged from flowering plants gathered together without regard to expense from every quarter of the globe."

Wynford Dewhurst, *Impressionist Painting: Its Genesis and Development,* 1904

Claude Monet (French, 1840-1926)
Waterlily Pond, 1904
Oil on canvas, 35^{7}/$_{16}$ x 36^{1}/$_{4}$ in.
Musée des Beaux-Arts de Caen

5

6

7

8

9

10

11

a native Californian, Guy Rose visited Giverny as early as 1890, and later relocated there from 1904 until 1912. Perhaps because of his friendship with Theodore Robinson, Rose enjoyed an acquaintance with Monet and received artistic criticism from him.

Guy Rose (American, 1867-1925)
Late Afternoon, Giverny, n.d.
Oil on canvas, 23¾ x 28¾ in.
San Diego Museum of Art

February

12 _____

13 _____

14 _____

15 _____

16 _____

17 _____

18 _____

Y ellow and red tulips emerge from a ground cover of blue forget-me-nots. These are the spring plantings on the raised beds in front of Monet's house.

Photo by Elizabeth Murray

February

19 _____

20 _____

21 _____

22 _____

23 _____

24 _____

25 _____

*f*ourteen paintings have been started at the same time – a study in scales, as it were – each the translation of a single, identical motif whose effect is modified by the time of day, the sun, and the clouds.

"This is where the Epte River flows into the Seine, among tiny islands shaded by tall trees, where branches of the river, like peaceful, solitary lakes beneath the foliage, form mirrors of water reflecting the greenery; this is where, since last summer, Claude Monet has been working..."

Maurice Guillemot, "Claude Monet," *La Revue Illustrée,* March 15, 1898

Claude Monet (French, 1840-1926)
Branch of the Seine near Giverny, 1897
Oil on canvas, 29½ x 36¾ in.
Musée du Louvre, Paris

Feb./March

26

27

28   29

1

2

3

4

*i*n 1900 Frederick Carl Frieseke began to summer in Giverny, and in 1906 he began to rent Theodore Robinson's former house next door to Monet. Although he lived so near to Monet, he seems not to have associated with him very much. Frieseke's work was influenced more by Auguste Renoir and Henri Fantin-Latour.

Frederick Carl Frieseke (American, 1874-1939)
The Garden Parasol, c. 1909
Oil on canvas, 57⅛ x 77 in.
North Carolina Museum of Art, Raleigh
Purchased with funds from the State of
North Carolina

5

6

7

8

9

10

11

awton Parker moved to Giverny in 1903 and lived next door to his good friend Frederick Frieseke. He had been a studio painter, but after settling in Giverny, he began *plein-air* painting in the Impressionistic style. His primary subject remained portraits, but at Giverny he began studying the effects of outdoor light on human figures.

Lawton Parker (American, 1868-1954)
Laurel, n.d.
Oil on board, 10 x 11$\frac{7}{8}$ in.
Florence Griswold Museum, Old Lyme,
Connecticut

12

13

14

15

16

17

18

m onet was inspired to build his Japanese-style footbridge from one of the many Hiroshige woodblock prints he collected. He later added the iron trellis and planted both blue and white wisteria to create a romantic focal point with beautiful reflections in his waterlily pond.

Photo by Elizabeth Murray

March

19 _____

20 _____

21 _____

22 _____

23 _____

24 _____

25 _____

"laughing at these memories and chain smoking, Claude Monet takes me into his garden. It's the one where he had a pond dug, which was the model for his *Water lilies*. At this time of year, the green leaves sleep nonchalantly on gray water, while the flowers the painter portrayed in his unforgettable series are hidden, gestating within the mysterious web of their sap."

André Arnyvelde, "At Home with the Painter of Light," *Je Sais Tout,* January 15, 1914

Claude Monet (French, 1840-1926)
The Waterlily Pond, Harmony in Green, 1899
Oil on canvas, 35 x 36½ in.
Musée du Louvre, Paris

26

27

28

29

30

31

1

"there are abundant irises of all varieties along the edges of the pond. In the spring there are *Iris siberica* and *virginica* with their long, velvety petals; later, Japanese iris *(Iris kaempferi)* abound and impart an oriental touch, which is further enhanced by such plants as Japanese tree peonies. Numerous specimens of these were sent to Claude Monet 20 years ago and have adjusted perfectly to the climate of Normandy."

Georges Truffaut, "The Garden of a Great Painter," *Jardinage,* November, 1924

Claude Monet (French, 1840-1926)
Irises by the Pond, c. 1920-24
Oil on canvas, 78½ x 59¼ in.
Virginia Museum of Fine Arts
Museum Purchase: The Williams Fund, 1971

April

2 _____

3 _____

4 _____

5 _____

6 _____

7 _____

8 _____

"*a*ll I did was to look at what the universe showed me, to let my brush bear witness to it. Is that nothing? Your error is to seek to reduce the world to your size, whereas the greater your understanding of things, the better your understanding of yourself. Give me your hand, and let us help one another to observe ever better.'"

Claude Monet as quoted by Georges Clemenceau in *Claude Monet,* 1929

Claude Monet with Lily Butler and Mrs. Kuroki
on the Japanese Bridge, 1921
Photo courtesy of the Musée Claude Monet

9

10

11

12

13

14

15

*b*oston artist Philip Leslie Hale began to abandon his dark, Spanish-influenced style for the light-filled Impressionistic aesthetic after visiting Giverny in 1887-88. He became one of the most important American Impressionists, not only in creating a large body of work, but also in his role as art critic for the Paris magazine *Arcadia* in 1892-93 and later for the Boston *Herald*.

Philip Leslie Hale (American, 1865-1931)
Poppies, n.d.
Oil on board, 21¼ x 25⅝ in.
Colby College Museum of Art
Gift of Mr. and Mrs. Ellerton M. Jetté

April

16

17

18

19

20

21

22

“*h*e does not have a studio as such. Living in the magnificent countryside of Giverny…he paints from morning to night. He remains out of doors in any sort of weather. A kind of barn into which a wide bay window has been cut serves as a storage place for his canvases; they are hung or piled up in corners there.”

Georges Jeanniot, “Notes on Art: Claude Monet,” *La Cravache Parisienne,* June 23, 1888

Claude Monet (French, 1840-1926)
Field of Poppies, Giverny, 1885
Oil on canvas, 23⅝ x 28¾ in.
Virginia Museum of Fine Arts
Collection of Mr. and Mrs. Paul Mellon, 85.499

April

23

24

25

26

27

28

29

*t*he green stairs lead to Monet's blue and white kitchen, where he and his cook prepared gourmet meals as delicious as Monet's gardens and paintings are exquisite. Guests and family would often dine on the terrace or in the garden in pleasant weather.

Photo by Elizabeth Murray

April/May

30

1

2

3

4

5

6

*m*onet's bedroom window was the perfect vantage point for review of his favorite masterpiece – his garden.

Photo by Elizabeth Murray

May

7 _____

8 _____

9 _____

10 _____

11 _____

12 _____

13 _____

"*q*uite an American colony has gathered, I am told, at Givernay [*sic*], seventy miles from Paris, on the Seine, the home of Claude Monet, including our Louis Ritter, W.L. Metcalf, Theodore Wendell [*sic*], John Breck, and Theodore Robinson. A few pictures just received from these young men show that they have got the blue-green color of Monet's impressionism and 'got it bad.'"

Critic in "Boston Art and Artists," *The Art Amateur* 17, October, 1887

Theodore Robinson (American, 1852-96)
Valley of the Seine from Giverny Heights, 1892
Oil on canvas, 25⅞ x 32⅛ in.
In the collection of The Corcoran Gallery of Art
Museum Purchase, Gallery Fund, 1900

May

14

15

16

17

18

19

20

“I suppose he has painted 'The Haystacks,' one of his most famous subjects, at least twenty times. They stood in a neighbor's field close to Monet's house....He portrayed them in summer, in the autumn, and in winter; in the morning, at noon, and at twilight; sometimes sparkling with dew, sometimes enveloped in fog, sometimes covered with frost, sometimes laden with snow; and though each picture was different from all the rest, one scarcely knew which to choose, they were all so true and beautiful.”

William H. Fuller, *Claude Monet and His Paintings*, 1899

Claude Monet (French, 1840-1926)
Haystack, 1893
Oil on canvas, 26 x 40 in.
Museum of Fine Arts, Springfield, Massachusetts
James Philip Gray Collection, 44.06

May

21

22

23

24

25

26

27

"**m.** Claude Monet's heart beats responsively as soon as he comes into contact with the intimate life of the out-of-doors. His enthusiasm animates his vision; he causes us to know and to love beauty everywhere, a beauty that eludes both a casual glance and scientific examination with lens and compass. It would be difficult to resist the appeal of an artist of such extraordinary sensitivity, who is so steeped in his work that he succeeds in making us share his own emotion, joy and humanism."

Roger Marx, "M. Claude Monet's 'Water Lilies'," *La Gazette des Beaux-Arts,* June, 1909

Claude Monet (French, 1840-1926)
In the Woods at Giverny – Blanche Hoschedé Monet at
her Easel with Suzanne Hoschedé Reading, 1885-90
Oil on canvas, 36 x 38½ in.
The Los Angeles County Museum of Art
Mr. and Mrs. George Garde De Sylva Collection

28

29

30

31

1

2

3

When Theodore Wendel returned to America from France in 1889, his exhibited works in Boston prompted critics to name him one of the most effective Impressionists. He is known to have painted in Giverny in 1886 and 1887.

Theodore Wendel (American, 1859-1932)
Girl with Turkeys, Giverny, 1886
Oil on canvas, 23½ x 29 in.
Sheldon Memorial Art Gallery
University of Nebraska-Lincoln
NAA – Gift of Beatrice D. Rohman

June

4

5

6

7

8

9

10

*L*arge blocks of color blend much like Monet would have applied brush strokes to his canvas. Dahlias, Asters, cosmos and stock create this tapestry effect.

Photo by Elizabeth Murray

June

11 _____

12 _____

13 _____

14 _____

15 _____

16 _____

17 _____

m auve-color tulips bloom among wedgewood-blue Dutch iris, providing early spring color under the old cherry tree, which was a part of Monet's original orchard.

Photo by Elizabeth Murray

June

18

19

20

21

22

23

24

t his path leads to Monet's second studio where he painted many of his works before the large waterlily paintings. He also built a garage for his car, a darkroom where he could experiment with photography and an apartment for his married stepdaughter.

Photo by Elizabeth Murray

June/July

25

26

27

28

29

30

1

*f*rederick Frieseke's wife was an enthusiastic gardener, and many of his paintings employed a feminine figure in a garden setting as their subject.

Frederick Carl Frieseke (American, 1874-1939)
Hollyhocks, c. 1914
Oil on canvas, 25½ x 32 in.
National Academy of Design, New York

July

2 _____

3 _____

4 _____

5 _____

6 _____

7 _____

8 _____

"'aside from painting and gardening,' he said to me, 'I'm good for nothing.'"

Maurice Kahn, "Claude Monet's Garden," *Le Temps,* June 7, 1904

Claude Monet (French, 1840-1926)
Boat at Giverny, c. 1887
Oil on canvas, 37^{13}/$_{16}$ x 51^{9}/$_{16}$ in.
Musée d'Orsay, Paris
Bequeathed by Princess Edmond de Polignac, 1944

July

9 _____

10 _____

11 _____

12 _____

13 _____

14 _____

15 _____

"We had arrived at the new studio. We entered, and my eyes widened in wonder. Claude Monet had enlarged his original motif with a nobility, an amplitude, and an instructive sense of decor that were totally unexpected. Utilizing a compositional process whose simplicity was one of the happiest of inspirations, he had depicted the water-lily pond from the perspective of the path that encircles it, and each of the vantage points he had selected was enclosed in the framework of one of the canvases....The whole scene shimmered with the brilliance of an already fading sun whose last rays were refulgent as floods of gold in a pearl gray and turquoise sky."

François Thiébault-Sisson,
"Claude Monet's
Water Lilies," *La Revue
de l'Art Ancien et Moderne,*
June, 1927

Claude Monet (French, 1840-1926)
Green Reflections (detail), 1914-1922
Oil on canvas, 77½ x 333½ in.
One of eight compositions comprising
Waterlilies. Study of Water.
First Waterlilies Room, Musée de l'Orangerie, Paris
Claude Monet donation, 1922

16

17

18

19

20

21

22

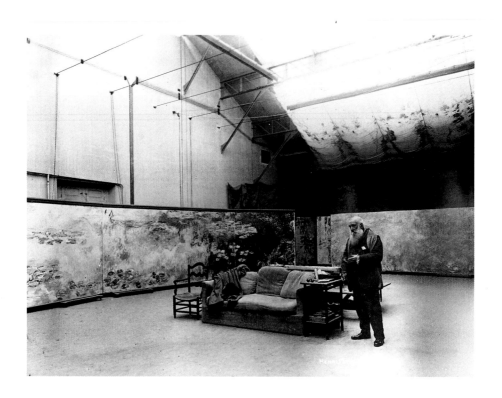

"*t*he *Water Lilies* panels show him desperately reaching to achieve the impossible. Volleys of luminous transparencies leap from his pulsing hand and bring forth new flaming radiances with loaded pigments....From close up, the canvas appears to be the prey of a bacchanal of incongruous colors; from the proper distance, these arrange themselves, fall in line, and combine to become a delicate construction of interpretative shapes within the precise and certain luminous order."

Georges Clemenceau, *Claude Monet*, 1929

Claude Monet posing in front of his huge waterlily
paintings in his third and final studio at Giverny,
c. 1924-25
Photo courtesy of the Musée Claude Monet

July

23 _____

24 _____

25 _____

26 _____

27 _____

28 _____

29 _____

"beyond the road and the unweeded path of the railroad track, along a brook flowing between the willows, Claude Monet has had a pool dug out, spanned by a wooden bridge in the Japanese style. Upon that immobile mirror float water lilies, aquatic plants, unique species with broad, spreading leaves and disquieting flowers of a strange exoticism. On either side are locks to allow a daily change of water. The locals were opposed at first, suspicious of this unfamiliar flower, claiming that the artist was poisoning the countryside, that their cows would no longer be able to drink."

Maurice Guillemot, "Claude Monet," *La Revue Illustrée,* March 15, 1898

Claude Monet (French, 1840-1926)
The Water Lily Pond, 1904
Oil on canvas, 35⅛ x 36⁵⁄₁₆ in.
Denver Art Museum, Helen Dill Collection 1935.14

July/August

30 _____

31 _____

1 _____

2 _____

3 _____

4 _____

5 _____

"**t**he leaves lie flat upon the surface of the water, and from among them blossom the yellow, blue, violet, and pink corollas of that lovely water flower. [The pond is spanned by] an arched wooden bridge painted green, near which Monet sets up his easel....The whole thing comes together to create a setting that enchants us rather than inspiring our awe, a dreamlike setting that is extremely oriental."

Louis Vauxcelles, "An Afternoon Visit with Claude Monet," *L'Art et les Artistes,* December, 1905

Claude Monet (French, 1840-1926)
The Waterlily Pond, Harmony in Pink, 1900
Oil on canvas, 35¼ x 39⅜ in.
Musée d'Orsay, Paris
Camondo bequest, 1911

6

7

8

9

10

11

12

f lame-color azaleas at the edge of the waterlily pond accent the pink house with Monet's huge barn-like studio in the background.

Photo by Elizabeth Murray

August

13

14

15

16

17

18

19

*L*ouis Ritman grew up in Chicago and studied at the Art Institute before he went to France in 1909. After studying in Paris for two to three years, he moved to Giverny, where he lived for about twenty years.

Louis Ritman (American, 1889-1963)
Nude Study No. 1, 1915
Oil on canvas, 36½ x 36½ in.
Des Moines Art Center
Gift of Mrs. Florence Carpenter, 1941

August

20

21

22

23

24

25

26

*g*uy Rose with Frederick Frieseke, Lawton Parker, Edmund Greacen, Richard Miller and Karl Anderson referred to themselves as "The Giverny Group" when they exhibited together in 1909/10. Rose's paintings depicted figures posed in misty landscapes rather than the usual bright floral settings favored by his contemporaries.

Guy Rose (American, 1867-1925)
Warm Afternoon, n.d.
Oil on canvas, 29 x 23½ in.
Collection of The Oakland Museum

27 _____

28 _____

29 _____

30 _____

31 _____

1 _____

2 _____

"If Bridgeman is Gérôme and water, Wendel is Monet and jam. But the new things that Monet and his imitators have to say, the colors and qualities which they constrain us to see by exaggerating them out of all proportion to facts are, at least, more entertaining than the weary old Gérômisms."

a critic in "Monthly Record of American Art," *Magazine of Art* 14, May, 1891

Theodore Wendel (American, 1858-1932)
Farm Scene, n.d.
Oil on board, 20⅛ x 15 in.
Colby College Museum of Art
Gift of Mr. and Mrs. Ellerton M. Jetté

September

3

4

5

6

7

8

9

r ed dahlias and blue salvia create strong vertical
lines in the foreground, while Monet's pink house
is framed with golden French sunflowers and blue sky.

Photo by Elizabeth Murray

September

10 _____

11 _____

12 _____

13 _____

14 _____

15 _____

16 _____

a Japanese cherry tree in full bloom cascades over the Epte river, the water source of Monet's pond. Monet had to convince local farmers and washer women that making the pond would not deplete the water supply and that his exotic waterlilies would not poison their cattle downstream.

Photo by Elizabeth Murray

September

17 _____

18 _____

19 _____

20 _____

21 _____

22 _____

23 _____

"*t*he Seine cuts its broad silver swath through the fields, a line of graceful poplars guards its edge, then comes a narrow strip of grass land, then the high-road – of that clean, smooth type that never fails to delight the traveller in France. Well back from the road and separated from it by the big cheery flower garden with its white fence, stands the house of Claude Monet. It is long and low, a solid, comfortable place."

Walter Pach, "At the Studio of Claude Monet," *Scribner's Magazine,* June, 1908

Claude Monet (French, 1840-1926)
The Seine at Giverny, Morning Mists, 1897
Oil on canvas, 35 x 36 in.
North Carolina Museum of Art, Raleigh
Purchased with funds from the North Carolina Art
Society and the Sarah Graham Kenan Foundation

September

24

25

26

27

28

29

30

"One should never forget that seeing and producing an effect of nature is not a matter of intellect, but of feeling…I avoid being conventional as much as possible."

Frieseke quoted in Clara T. MacChesney, "Frieseke Tells Some of the Secrets of His Art," *New York Times,* June 7, 1914

Frederick Carl Frieseke (American, 1874-1939)
Giverny Landscape, 1915-16
Oil on canvas, 30 x 25 in.
In the collection of The Corcoran Gallery of Art
Gift of George Biddle, 1960

October

1

2

3

4

5

6

7

*l*ooking through a red azalea across the pond one
  discovers a pleasing view of the small footbridge
and blooming cherry tree.

Photo by Elizabeth Murray

October

8

9

10

11

12

13

14

"*a* small wooden bridge painted green extends across the pond. A boat is moored to it. All around the pond are water irises, and behind them are azaleas, tamarisk trees, a weeping willow."

Maurice Kahn, "Claude Monet's Garden," *Le Temps,* June 7, 1904

Claude Monet (French, 1840-1926)
Waterlilies and Japanese Bridge
Oil on canvas, 31⅝ x 31⁵/₁₆ in.
The Art Museum, Princeton University
From the Collection of William Church Osborn,
Class of 1883, Trustee of Princeton University
(1914-1951), President of the Metropolitan Museum
of Art (1941-1947); gift of his family

October

15

16

17

18

19

20

21

a utumn creates a new palette of colors around
Monet's waterlily pond. Liquidambar are like
red tongues of fire among more subdued greens.

Photo by Elizabeth Murray

October

22 _____

23 _____

24 _____

25 _____

26 _____

27 _____

28 _____

"*n*otwithstanding his sixty years, Claude Monet is robust and hearty as an oak. His face has been weathered by wind and sun; his dark hair is flecked with white; his shirt collar is open; and his clear, steel gray eyes are sharp and penetrating – they are the kind of eyes that seem to look into the very depths of things....He has the exquisite and affable manners of a gentleman farmer."

Louis Vauxcelles, "An Afternoon Visit with Claude Monet," *L'Art et les Artistes,* December 1905

Claude Monet, 1901
Photo courtesy of the Musée Claude Monet

29

30

31

1

2

3

4

*i*n 1892 Theodore Butler married Monet's stepdaughter Suzanne Hoschedé-Monet. He had come to Giverny with his good friend Theodore Robinson, and he remained there permanently, working in an Impressionist manner greatly influenced by Monet. Suzanne died in 1895, and Butler married her sister, Marthe, four years later.

Theodore Earl Butler (American, 1860-1936)
A Tiller of Soil, 1894
Oil on canvas, 23½ x 28¾ in.
Columbus Museum of Art, Ohio
Bequest of Alfred L. Willson

5

6

7

8

9

10

11

*i*n early June the first waterlilies bloom. Monet had waterlilies of every color almost covering the pond's surface. The water gardener was instructed to keep the edges trimmed so that the sky and clouds could be reflected between the lilies.

Photo by Elizabeth Murray

November

12

13

14

15

16

17

18

*t*his shade of purple-pink aster (Michaelmas daisy) glows on grey misty mornings and in the twilight hours when other colors fade away.

Photo by Elizabeth Murray

November

19 _____

20 _____

21 _____

22 _____

23 _____

24 _____

25 _____

"**W**hen the sunlight plays upon the water, it resembles – damascened as it is with the water lilies' great round leaves, and encrusted with the precious stones of their flowers – the masterwork of a goldsmith who has melded alloys of the most magical metals."

Arsène Alexandre, "Monet's Garden," *Le Figaro,* August 9, 1901

Claude Monet (French, 1840-1926)
Water Lilies, c. 1914
Oil on canvas, 63¼ x 71⅛ in.
Collection of the Portland Art Museum,
Oregon Art Institute
Helen Thurston Ayer Fund

26

27

28

29

30

1

2

"Called on Monet...he spoke of stupid people saying, 'You are going to finish that, you are not going to leave that comme ça.' Mais pourquoi pas? Why not indeed. And who is the judge when to stop, if not the painter. This exhortation of others to 'finish that' has weighed on me all my life."

Theodore Robinson, diary entry, August 14, 1892. Frick Art Reference Library, New York

Theodore Robinson (American, 1852-96)
Scene at Giverny, 1890
Oil on canvas, 16 x 25¾ in.
© The Detroit Institute of Arts
Gift of Mrs. Christian H. Hecker

December

3 _____

4 _____

5 _____

6 _____

7 _____

8 _____

9 _____

"he same man we find to be somewhat laconic and cold in Paris is completely different here: kindly, unperturbed, enthusiastic. When he has reason to come into the land of the boulevards, his smile is more than a little mocking and sarcastic; in his garden, among his flowers, he glows with benevolence. For months at a time, this artist forgets that Paris even exists; his gladioli and dahlias sustain him with their superb refinements – but cause him to forget civilization."

Arsène Alexandre,
"Monet's Garden," *Le Figaro,*
August 9, 1901

Claude Monet, c. 1913
Photo courtesy of the Musée Claude Monet

December

10

11

12

13

14

15

16

a regal carpet, woven with various shades of golden English wallflowers, is planted in Monet's orchard under cherry, plum and apple trees. Ruby-colored columbine sparkle like jewels among sapphire-blue iris and tourmaline-pink tulips.

Photo by Elizabeth Murray

December

17

18

19

20

21

22

23

"i f...I can someday see M. Claude Monet's garden, I feel sure that I shall see something that is not so much a garden of flowers as of colors and tones, less of an old-fashioned flower garden than a color garden, so to speak, one that achieves an effect not entirely nature's, because it was planted so that only the flowers with matching colors will bloom at the same time, harmonize in an infinite stretch of blue or pink."

Marcel Proust, "Splendors," *Le Figaro,* June 15, 1907

Claude Monet (French, 1840-1926)
The Artist's Garden at Giverny, 1900
Oil on canvas, 35¼ x 36¼ in.
Yale University Art Gallery
Gift of Mr. and Mrs. Paul Mellon, B.A. 1929

December

24

25

26

27

28

29

30   31